D1626357

Why the Rabbit stamps its foot

By Robin Page · Illustrated by John Paley

BIRD'S FARM
BOOKS

Robin Page was born and bred on the farm where he still lives. Wildlife – the birds, animals, insects and flowers around him have been a life-long love. He has written twenty-one books for adults, and contributes to various national newspapers and magazines. He is Chairman and founder of The Countryside Restoration Trust.

John Paley is a Yorkshireman living in Norfolk. He trained at the Scarborough School of Art. Real life was an even better teacher and he has become one of Britain's best wildlife and landscape painters. He has held many exhibitions and illustrated numerous books. *Why the Rabbit Stamps its Foot* is his first book for children.

First published in 2000 by Bird's Farm Books
Barton, Cambs. CB3 7AG

Text © Robin Page, 2000
Illustrations © John Paley, 2000

ISBN   0 905232 17 8

Designed by Jim Reader

Design and production in association with
Book Production Consultants plc
25–27 High Street, Chesterton, Cambridge CB4 1ND

Printed and bound by Proost NV, Turnhout, Belgium

In those dim and distant days before men painted pictures, rabbits looked almost like miniature kangaroos. They hopped, they flopped, they jumped and they bumped; they even sat up on their back legs to watch the world go by, in exactly the same way as kangaroos do today. They ate like kangaroos too – and still do – holding juicy stems of grass, spinach and carrots with their front paws to nibble, and then,

when they had finished, they washed and brushed themselves by licking their paws and whiskers – before hopping off home for a snooze. This is not surprising for, although many people have forgotten, the rabbit was once thought to be a long lost cousin of the kangaroo – and it could be true.

In fact the only real difference to be seen between the small cuddly rabbit and the large cuddly kangaroo was that the rabbit had a tiny, fluffy tail, while the kangaroo had a large, long unfluffy brown tail.

It was because the rabbit looked rather like a kangaroo that it was once taken all the way to Australia. Travellers wanted the two to meet, and that is why the rabbit and the kangaroo still get on so well together in many parts of the great Australian outback. It also explains why rabbits dislike swimming – the long voyage to Australia made them feel very seasick.

On a few of the boats to Australia some rabbits escaped from their cages, and not knowing any better, they began digging for freedom. When they hit the sea, the water rushed in creating great salty fountains of sea-water and, despite the titanic efforts of the sailors to bale out, the boats, the rabbits and the sailors all sank beneath the great Pacific Ocean. That is why sailors today never say 'rabbits'.

They believe that it brings them bad luck. They won't even say 'rabbits' on the first day of every new month. Instead they wake up and say 'Pinch, Punch the First Day of the Month', and hope to stay afloat.

It was in those far off dim and distant days before men painted pictures that the kangaroo and rabbit appeared in the world. Then, there was just one large continent surrounded by sea. The kangaroo lived in the South, the rabbit lived in the middle and the hedgehog, who was still the 'Hairless-hog' lived in the North. There were other animals too, of course, but they do not concern us here.

One day the world began to crack. The huge island of Gondwanaland split into continents and islands and the one great ocean became divided into seven distant seas. The kangaroos were marooned on a vast island-continent that drifted even further south, called Australia. The hedgehogs drifted north, on what we now call Europe, and the rabbit stayed in the middle on what became known as Spain and North-West Africa.

Because the men in those dim and distant days painted no pictures and saw no pictures, nobody knew that the rabbit looked like a small kangaroo, and because Australia had drifted so far away, nobody had even heard of Australia or kangaroos.

But the rabbit was like the kangaroo; it sat up, it hopped and it bounced along – it loved bouncing, and when it had to go anywhere it never thought to walk or run – it bounced. It bounced to feed, it bounced to play and it bounced home in the evening where it bounced into bed and bounced out again in the morning.

The one big difference between the small cuddly rabbit and the large cuddly kangaroo was in the way it reared its children. The female rabbit loved children and had large families; the kangaroo preferred a quieter life and so had her children just one at a time. Where the rabbit lived there were plenty of boulders with holes and small caves between them, so the mother could make a warm, cosy and comfortable nest for her babies.

But where the kangaroo bounced and bounded along it was flat. With no rocks in which to hide and the ground was too dry and hard to dig a hole or build a house. So God provided the female kangaroo with a pouch, like a snug natural handbag, in which to carry her single baby. It made sense; if a rabbit had been given a pouch large enough for seven babies to snuggle up inside, she would have become so heavy that she would not have been able to bounce.

It was one of the most pleasant sights possible to see a family of bouncing rabbits, bouncing along in single file. When danger threatened the rabbits would bounce higher, further and longer. Their back feet would stamp onto the ground and their legs would actually twang like a spring. They would bounce over boulders; they would bounce from the top of one rock to another, and they could bounce further and faster than any of their enemies could run.

Now it so happened that in the not too dim and distant days of historic time, the Romans loved rabbits. They enjoyed seeing them bounce and they

gave rabbits to their friends as presents. Sometimes famous Roman soldiers, runners and jumpers, would even eat rabbits, hoping that rabbit stew would make them bounce too. They caught them in great high nets which only the fittest and cleverest rabbits could bounce over.

At that time there were no rabbits in Britain, and when the Romans arrived, they missed seeing their little bouncing friends. So Gallus Oryctolagus Cuniculus, the Governor General of Britain, sent a message to the Emperor Caesar, in his great palace in Rome, asking for rabbits. Bouncing rabbits would make Britain a happier more attractive place, he said, and they would help cure his soldiers of homesickness.

Four rabbits were sent; one male – the buck – and his three wives – the does. They were released into a large grassy field in Kent; the Romans were pleased, the rabbits were pleased and the ancient Britons were amazed – they had never seen such bouncing animals before. The rabbits loved it; English grass was much greener, fresher and tastier than the dry coarse grass of Africa, Spain and Rome, and they quickly grew fat. The females got fatter still and soon babies were born.

Now rabbits grow much faster than Romans, Ancient Britons, Modern Britons, and even Australians and within 16 weeks the baby rabbits were having baby rabbits and soon the babies of the babies were having babies, and then they had babies and more babies and so it went on – a rabbit population explosion took place.

Within a year there were more than a thousand rabbits and to prevent over crowding and to stop all the beautiful grass from being eaten they began to bounce to different parts of England. By the end of the second year rabbits had bounced as far as Bedford, Bude and Bicester and one family had even bounced to where Buckingham Palace stands today.

There would have been even more rabbits, but there was just one problem. In Africa and Spain the rabbits were surrounded by boulders to bounce over, to escape from their enemies. In England they found fields and woods, with fewer hiding places and fewer things to bounce over.

They also discovered that by eating lush English grass they became heavier and so they could not bounce so high.

Consequently, not only were the rabbits getting fat, but so were the foxes, who were catching the overweight rabbits to eat them.

Some of the fat rabbits dug holes, called burrows, in the soft English soil, to hide in. But there was another problem; how do you bounce into a burrow, particularly when you are being chased? The rabbits could not get used to them, and every time they bounced home they banged their heads.

They received cut eyes, cross eyes, black eyes, cuts, bruises, concussion, confusion, headaches, neckaches, backache and toothache, and the more they banged their heads, the more it made their front teeth stick out.

It was terrible; they had no headache pills, doctors or dentists. Because it was so long ago, instead, they had to find willow trees and chew the bark. That acted like medicine and gave them relief. Many years later a wise old man with no teeth copied the rabbits, sucking the bark through his gums. He discovered that the bark of the willow tree really did cure headaches, for it contained a natural type of aspirin, which was later put into pills.

Fortunately, outside a burrow in Barton, a small rabbit warren near Cambridge – a town in England that grew famous for attracting clever people – there was a quiet, thoughtful rabbit called Stanley. He had to be quiet and thoughtful as he was always banging his head when he bounced home and he had one never-ending headache. One day, as he was sitting by a large tree, dreaming of carrots, he saw a blue tit fly into a hole in the trunk above him where it had a nest.

'It didn't bounce in, hitting its head, it flew in head first,' Stanley said to himself excitedly. 'If we went into our holes head first we wouldn't bang our heads and we would always escape from the foxes.' Then he became sad, as he remembered that rabbits could not fly.

As he bounced slowly home, he nodded to his cousin, the hare. He was racing by at top speed, zig-zagging as he went and leaving a great trail of dust. Hares could run so fast that they did not need to live underground like their relations. The rabbits did not like them very much; every March they seemed to go quite mad, and they rushed everywhere at top speed, instead of bouncing and enjoying the journeys.

Suddenly Stanley stopped – that was it. If he ran like his head-strong cousin, instead of bouncing, he could go into his burrow head first, like a blue tit, and he would never bang his head again. But how do you run, when all you have done throughout your life is bounce? He stamped his back feet as if to bounce and then pushed himself forwards onto his front feet. He fell over awkwardly and rolled into some stinging nettles. He tried again, he stumbled and then he ran.

He had never run before. It was strange – a bit low down and you couldn't see the countryside; it was rather like riding a racing bike, after an ordinary bike, but it was fun. He rested, hopped and then tried again, stamping his back feet to remind himself not to bounce, but to tip forwards and run. He ran, he raced, he roared, he romped and he rushed, until he could not think of another word beginning with 'r', and he then ran rapidly to his favourite anthill to get a good view of the sunset.

He froze. 'Fox', his brother Roger shouted. Stanley was frightened. He stamped his back feet loudly, to remind himself to run, and he ran. He stamped so loudly that all those rabbits who had not heard the warning felt the vibrations and looked up and saw the fox. They bounced off towards their burrows.

Stanley ran, weaving in and out of his bouncing relations, and overtaking his mother and father, sisters and brothers, including Roger. He could run so fast that he dived into the burrow well ahead of the others. Soon they all followed, banging their heads as they tumbled in. They moaned and groaned as they rolled on the floor but they had all beaten the fox, thanks to Stanley's stamping. They had all received throbbing headaches too – all that is except Stanley.

Stanley was a hero. All that evening, in the moonlight, he was teaching the other members of the warren to stamp and run, not bounce, and in times of danger and trouble rabbits have been running ever since.

Because of this, when Stanley married he proudly called his first son Thumper – he could thump his feet louder than any rabbit had ever thumped his feet before.

Today, if you look closely, you will still notice that rabbits stamp their back feet when they are frightened. They do it to remind themselves to run, not to bounce, and quite by accident it warns all the other rabbits of danger at the same time.